W9-DGY-803

THEN I THINK OF GOD

First Printing, November 1942
Second Printing, December 1943
Third Printing, October 1944
Fourth Printing, October 1945
Fifth Printing, February 1947
Sixth Printing, September 1947
Seventh Printing, July 1949
Eighth Printing, May 1951

Printed in the United States of America

THEN I THINK OF GOD

A Book of Devotional Readings for Children

BY

MABEL A. NIEDERMEYER

Illustrated by Carmon V. Livsey

THE BETHANY PRESS
ST. LOUIS 3, MISSOURI

IN

LOVING MEMORY

OF

MY FATHER AND MY MOTHER

A "Thank-You" Prayer

Thank you, God, for fathers and mothers who help us know and understand your love through the love in their own lives. Thank you for my own father and mother and for the Christian home which they helped us all to build together. Amen.

Contents

DEAR BOYS AND GIRLS:

A friend of mine once said, "Whenever I see a lilac bush in bloom, then I think of God and the beauty He has made in the world."

There are times when all of us think of God like that. It may be when something pleasant has happened to us, or when we have found something new and interesting or beautiful in God's world. Or it may be sometime when we need God's help to do what we know is right. Then there are the times when we just want to think about Him and talk with Him.

This book has been written especially for you to use at such times as these. You can read it alone and then talk with someone about what you have read. Or perhaps Mother or Daddy or an older brother or sister will read it with you and talk with you about it. Or if your family worships together in your home, you may like to use this book at those times.

You will not want to read it as you do a storybook. This is not that kind of book. It is made up of very short stories which might have happened to boys and girls like yourselves. Each story is followed by a prayer and a verse or two from the Bible. You perhaps will want to read only one story at a time. Then you may use the prayer as your own, and learn the Bible verse and try to do what it says.

The stories and prayers and Bible verses have been marked for different seasons and months of the year. That is because some of the stories happen at certain times of the year, like Christmas coming in December. You may want to read the stories and prayers month by month, or you may want to read them at just any time of the year.

The last few pages of this book are your very own. On them you may write about the times when you think of God. Like, "I thought of God today when I saw a rainbow in the sky." Or there may be times when you will want to write a prayer or another Bible verse that you have learned. Or perhaps you might see a beautiful picture which reminds you of God and his love for us. You could paste that on one of these pages, too.

I hope that you will like this book, and that the stories and verses and prayers will help you to know and understand God better.

Sincerely,

Your friend,

Mabel Niedermeyer

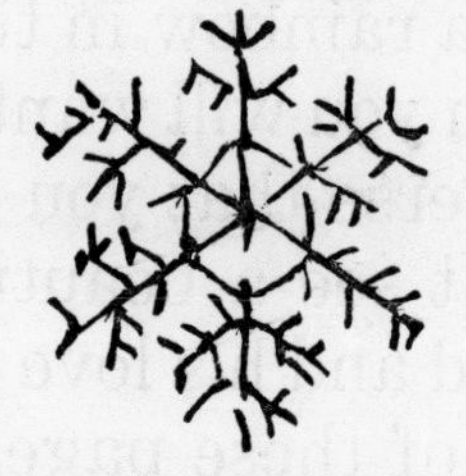

A Song of Creation

In the beginning, God made the heaven and the earth.

O sing unto the Lord,
For he hath done marvelous things.

And God made the day and the night, and the sun to shine by day and the moon and the stars to shine by night.

O sing unto the Lord,
For he hath done marvelous things.

And God made the oceans and the lakes and the rivers and the seas.

O sing unto the Lord,
For he hath done marvelous things.

And God made the grass and the trees and the plants and the flowers to grow on the land.

O sing unto the Lord,
For he hath done marvelous things.

And God made the birds to fly in the heaven and the fish to swim in the waters.

O sing unto the Lord,
For he hath done marvelous things.

And God made animals of every kind to live upon the earth.

O sing unto the Lord,
For he hath done marvelous things.

And God made man to enjoy the world which he had made.

O sing unto the Lord,
For he hath done marvelous things.

Snowflake Patterns

It began snowing today. I put on my snow suit and Daddy and I went out for a walk. I tried to catch the snowflakes as they fell. They made pretty patterns on my blue mittens. But they did not last very long. They soon melted away.

"I wish they would not melt so quickly," I told Daddy. "I want to see them."

"If you could keep them all," Daddy said, "you would find that they are all different."

"How do you mean, different?" I wanted to know.

"They are different in shape and size and pattern," Daddy answered. "Some are big, and some are little. Some look like wheels, and some look like stars. Still others look like spider webs."

Daddy caught a few just then and showed them to me.

"Look," he said. "Can you see the different designs in these flakes in my hand?"

I looked quickly before the snowflakes melted away.

"Yes," I said. "I wonder how God thought about making them all different like that."

I guess Daddy wondered, too, because he said, "God has thought of many things which we cannot understand."

A Prayer of Wonder

I wonder more and more about you, God, when I learn more about the world which you have made. I am glad for the snow and for the different patterns in the snowflakes. They help me to know you better. Amen.

A Bible Verse to Remember

The works of the Lord are great.

—Psalm 111:2a.

Electric Trains

David got a new electric train for Christmas. He has lots of tracks and switches and signals. He has a station and a tunnel, too.

I got an electric train for Christmas. But mine is not as big as David's train. I have only one set of tracks and none of the extra things that David has.

David always has bigger and more things than I do. Mother says it is because his father earns more money than my Daddy does. Then David has no brothers or sisters. Daddy has three of us to care for—Mildred and Dick and me—besides Mother and himself.

I like the way Mother talked with me about this. She said we do not need so many things to play with because we have each other. She also said that we cannot be happy with what we have if we are wanting something else.

I guess that means my wanting a train like David's. Sometimes I *almost* wish I had one like his. But I like my train, too. Dick helped me build a tower and a signal out of his electro set. He said we could build a bridge, too. That will be fun. More fun than having a ready-made bridge for the train to cross.

Yes, I am sure I shall be happy with my train and not want a big one like David's at all.

A Prayer for Understanding

Dear God, help me to understand that I cannot always have the things that my friends have. Or the things that I see in the stores. Help me to be happy with what I do have. Make me thankful for everything that is my own. And God, help me to know that friends and families and doing things together are more important than just having things. Amen.

A Bible Verse to Remember

Be content with such things as ye have.

—Hebrews 13:5b.

Feeding the Birds

We have some bird friends who come to visit us every day. They are snowbirds. They come for the crumbs that we put out for them. Daddy and Don built a feeding table in the yard.

Each morning after breakfast I try to remember to pick up the left-over crumbs and crusts of toast. I break them up in small pieces and then put them out on the feeding table. I do not have to wait for the snowbirds to come. Sometimes they are waiting for me. They flutter and flutter around and then settle down for the crumbs. They never leave until every single one has been picked up.

I forgot to put their food out for them today. So they flew up to the window sill as if to ask me what was the matter. They tapped the glass with their wings. Then they flew back to the feeding table.

"Have you forgotten us? We are still here waiting for you," they seemed to say.

Then I hurried to find some crumbs. Mother had some suet, too, which she gave me to give to them. They liked that. I was glad we could give it to them to make up for my forgetting the crumbs.

I am sorry that I forgot to feed these friends of ours today. The snow is hard and crusty. They may not find food any place else when I forget.

A Prayer for Help to Remember

Dear God, help me to remember to do my work each day. Show me ways that I can help you take care of the birds and other things that you have made. I am glad that I can be one of your workers. Amen.

A Bible Verse to Remember

My Father worketh . . . . and I work.

—John 5:17.

Sickness

I have been sick with the measles. I have not really been very sick. Only for the first three or four days. But I have had to stay in bed and keep warm. I have to be in a dark room, too, to protect my eyes from the light.

The doctor came to see me twice. Mother called him over the phone the other day. He told her what to do for me.

I like the way Mother takes care of me when I am sick. She knows just what to do and say. She knows when I want company and when I want to be alone. I like the way she gives me my medicine, too. Some of it does not taste very good, but I don't mind taking it at all when she gives it to me. She tells me that it will be bitter, and that I should swallow it quickly. Then she gives me a drink of orange juice to take the bad taste away.

Since I have been feeling better, Mother has been reading to me some. She tells me about the pictures, too. I will look at the pictures in the book when I am well again. But now I can almost see them the way Mother tells me about them. I close my eyes and listen, and then make up the pictures as she describes them. Mother even tells me their colors, and I can see them, too. It is just like a game when we do it this way.

I know that I am taking a lot of Mother's time from her work. When I get well again, I shall try to help her more.

A Prayer of Thanks

Thank you, God, for the way in which my mother takes care of me when I am sick. Thank you, too, for doctors who help to make sick people well. Help me to be pleasant and patient and to take my medicine willingly. Amen.

A Bible Verse to Remember

Do all things without murmurings.

—Philippians 2:14.

Faraway Friends

Miss Brown told us more about the children of China today. She said they are hungry and need food. She told us we could help them have rice to eat by sending money.

"How much money does it take to buy rice for them?" I asked.

"Just now one penny of our money will buy enough rice for a meal for one child," Miss Brown answered.

A penny did not seem very much to us. That would not buy a meal here in our country. I thought of the money I had in my bank. I wanted to use some of it in this way.

"I can bring some money to send," I said. "Can we send it ourselves?"

"Yes," Miss Brown told me. "I have a bank that we can keep it in until we have enough to send. Then we can get a money order and send it to the relief agency."

"I can bring some money,"

Bill said. Then Joe and some of the girls said they could help, too.

So we are going to bring as much money as we can to school every day. I am going to ask Mother if I can give a penny of my allowance every day. I am sure she will like to have me do that. It makes me feel nearer to these faraway friends when I can help them in this way.

A "Thinking-Out-Loud" Prayer

Dear God, I am thinking of the Chinese boys and girls who go to bed hungry at nights. I want to share with them so they may have food to eat. Make me willing to do without something I may want so that I can give some of my money to buy rice for them. Amen.

A Bible Verse to Remember

Freely ye have received, freely give.

—Matthew 10:8b.

Thanks for Coal

It was chilly in our house when I got up this morning. The wind had been blowing and whistling outside all night. It is warmer inside now. It began to grow warmer soon after Daddy took care of the furnace. He added several more shovels of coal just before he left for work.

I am glad that we have coal to burn. I asked Daddy once where it came from.

"From down in the earth," he said. "It takes millions and millions of years for it to form."

"But what makes it form?" I wanted to know.

Then Daddy told me about God's plan for coal. He said that dead trees and plants and ferns were pressed together to form coal in some parts of the earth. He also told me about the men who mine the coal for us to burn.

Then we began to think about all the workers who help us to have coal. First there are the men who discover the beds of coal and who build the mines. Then there are those who make the picks and other tools used in mining. Other builders make the little cars which bring the loose coal out of the ground.

The coal dealer is important, too. He buys tons

and tons of coal and fills our orders. Then the drivers of the trucks bring coal to our houses.

There must be many other workers, too. Without all of them we would not have the coal which God has planned for our use. I think they are working with God by helping us to have coal, don't you?

A Prayer of Thanks for Coal

Thank you, God, for coal to keep our houses warm. Thank you for all the workers who help to mine our coal and who get it ready for us to burn. Help us to find a way for everyone to have coal to keep warm in cold weather. Amen.

A Bible Verse to Remember

For we are God's fellow-workers.

—1 Corinthians 3:9a.

Quiet Friends

There is a man living in our block who sits in his window all day long. He is in a wheel chair. He always waves at me when I go by. I always wave back at him. He is my friend.

Sometimes after school I stop in to see him. I climb up in his chair with him. Then we talk together. I tell him all about school, and he tells me stories. Then sometimes we just sit without talking at all. He puts his arm around me and I sit very close to him. I lay my head on his chest so close I can feel him breathing. We like to sit that way and just look out of the window together. I know sometimes he is thinking about when he was a boy as I am. He tells me what he did then. He speaks very softly, but I can always understand what he says.

Tomorrow is Valentine's Day. I am making a valentine to give to this friend. It is a red heart with lace paper on it. There are flowers and birds on it, too. Inside is a verse which my sister helped me write. It is about friends.

I am not going to give him his valentine as soon as I stop tomorrow. I am going to make him guess what I have for him. Then I will crawl up in his chair. Maybe we will talk. Maybe we will just sit together thinking. . . . I hope that we will just sit quietly together for a while.

A Prayer of Quiet Gladness

I am glad, God, for quiet friends. I like the "rested-inside" feeling I have when I go to visit them. Show me ways of making them happy too. Amen.

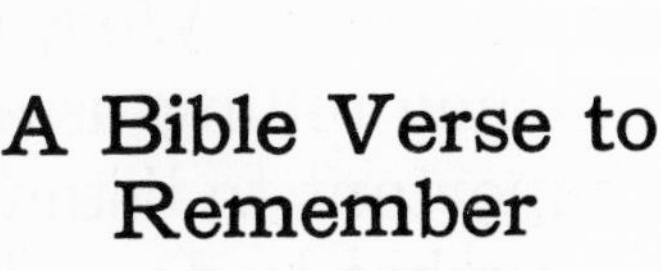

A Bible Verse to Remember

Love one another as I have loved you.

—John 15:12.

Our Best Work

We are making a moving picture of the stories of Jesus in my class at Sunday School. We are using the pictures from our lesson leaflets.

The "movie" is to be a surprise for the other boys and girls in the department. We are going to show it to them when it is finished. Jack will tell them about it while Grace and Kenneth turn the pictures.

We have been working hard for several weeks. Miss Moore has been showing us how. We wanted to begin even before she finished telling us about it. But she told us it was important to listen first and then we would know just what to do and how to do it.

It was fun choosing just what you wanted to do. We were soon busy. Some of us got in a hurry to get through. We did not do our work as well as we could. Several of the pictures were not pasted on the paper straight. Miss Moore had to remind us not to hurry with our work. She said we

should be sure to do our very best. I did some of my work over after she said that because I knew I could do better than I had done. We also took the crooked pictures off and pasted them on straight. Miss Moore said they looked much better then.

Our work is about finished. Miss Moore said that we can be proud of what we have done because it is our best work.

A Prayer for Help

Dear God, I am glad for work that I can do. Help me always to do my best work. Keep me from hurrying to get my work done. Thank you for the happy feeling which comes when I know I have done my best. Amen.

A Bible Verse to Remember

Learn to do well.

—Isaiah 1:17.

Kite Flying

Daddy and I flew our kite in the park today. Other boys and their fathers were there, too. It was fun to watch the kites go soaring up in the sky.

We made our kite in our basement. Daddy said it is the kind he used to fly when he was a boy.

"The wind is just right to try out our kite," he said at breakfast this morning. "That is unless Mother has some other plans for us to think about for this evening."

"Run along and fly your kite," Mother laughed. "I will have dinner ready when you get back."

I was waiting when Daddy came home from work. It was not long until we were out in the park. Daddy held the string of the kite first. He showed me how to hold the kite and then to let it go when he called to me. I

tried to do just what he said. When I let go, up, up, up went our kite.

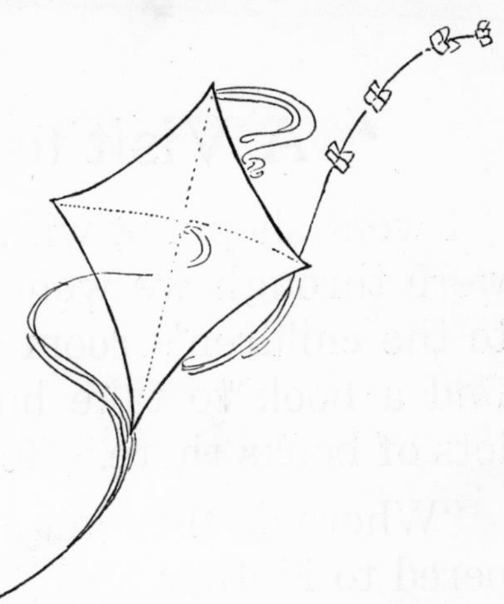

"It works, Daddy! It works!" I cried.

Daddy laughed as he hauled the kite down again. Then I held the string and ran with the kite as Daddy told me to do. Up, up, up, the wind carried it for a second time. It was lots of fun. I liked to feel the tug of the kite on the string. I liked to feel the wind blowing in my face and through my hair, too.

I think that God must be glad that we can use his wind for flying kites.

A Prayer of Gladness

I am glad for the wind, God. I am glad that it catches my kite and carries it up against the sky. I am glad for the tug on the string of the kite as it goes higher and higher. Amen.

A Bible Verse to Remember

He causeth his wind to blow.

—Psalm 147:18.

A Visit to the Library

I went shopping with Mother today. When we were through we went to the library. We went to the children's room there. Mother helped me find a book to take home to read. There were lots of books there. Rows and rows to pick from.

"Where do they get all of these books?" I whispered to Mother.

"From book stores and companies," she answered softly.

"But where do they get them? Where do the stories come from?" I wanted to know.

"Men and women write them for boys and girls like you to enjoy," Mother said. "Then they sell their stories to other people who have them printed in books. The library buys the books for people to read. They come here to get them just as we came today."

I looked again at the book which I had chosen. It was full of lovely colored pictures.

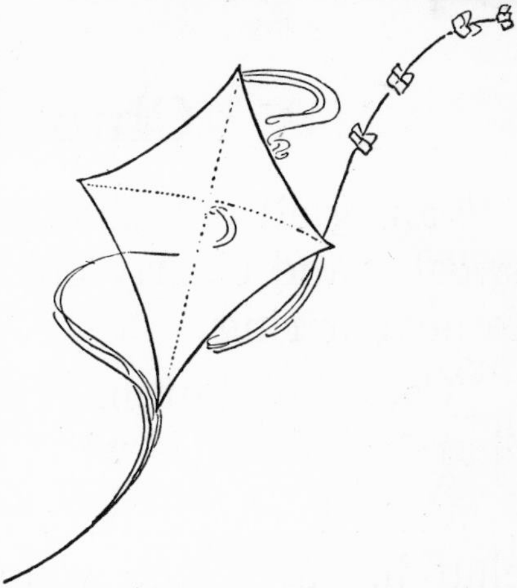

"And the pictures?" I asked. "Do men and women draw them for us, too?"

"Yes," was Mother's reply again. "Before the stories are put into books, some artist draws the pictures for them."

"I wish I could see all those people who help make our books," I said. "I would like to tell them 'thank you.' "

A Prayer of Thanks for Books

Thank you, God, for libraries of books so that everybody can read. I am glad I found out where our books come from. Help the people who write stories for boys and girls to know that we thank them. We are glad for the artists, too. Amen.

A Bible Verse to Remember

In everything give thanks; for this is the will of God.

—1 Thessalonians 5:18a.

Church Bells

I am glad our church has a bell. It rings so sweetly and clearly on Sunday mornings. I like to hear it ring.

"Come to church. Come to church. Come to church." That is what it seems to be saying.

When it rings the people begin to go into the church. Men and women, and boys and girls. Everybody in our block goes to church.

Just before our classes begin, the church bell rings again.

"Come and learn. Come and learn. Come and learn." That is what it seems to be saying this time.

We do learn at our church. We learn to sing new songs. We learn about God and we talk with him. We learn about ways in which we can help each other.

We learn about boys and girls who are going to church in other countries, too.

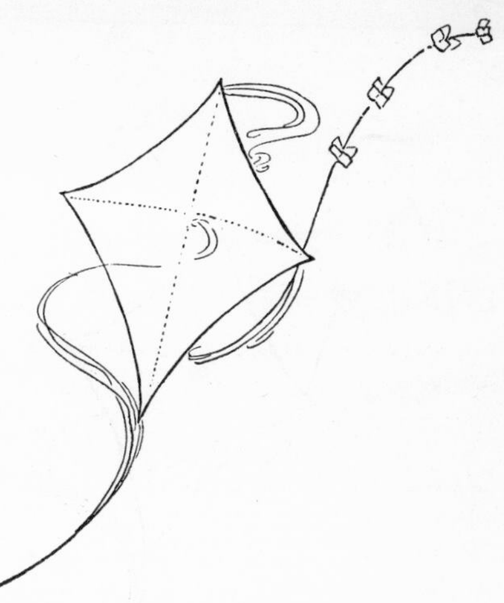

We learn from our minister. We learn from our teachers. We learn from each other. That is why our church bell seems to be telling us to "come and learn."

I like to go to church and learn. I am glad when I hear the church bell ring "Come to church" and "Come and learn." I am glad when Sunday comes.

A Sunday Prayer

Thank you, God, for our church. Thank you for Sundays when we go to church to learn. Thank you for the workers who help us to learn the stories in the Bible and how to help each other. Thank you, too, for our church bell which calls us to come to church and learn. Amen.

A Bible Verse to Remember

I was glad when they said unto me,
Let us go into the house of the Lord.

—Psalm 122:1.

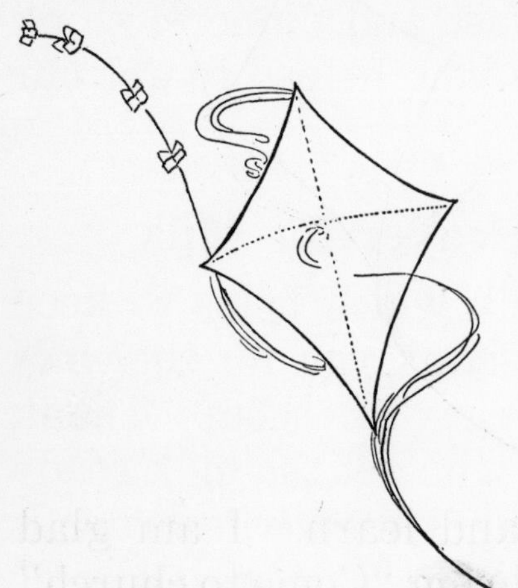

Thanks for Milk

We are learning about the story of milk at school. First there is the cow which gives us milk. But the cow has to be cared for by the farmer. She has to have good pasture land where she can find grass to eat. She has to be kept well and clean so that her milk will be pure and healthful. She has to have hay to eat, too, and a clean barn in which to stay when she is not in the pasture. The farmers take care of all of these. They help us to have milk to drink.

Then there are the workers in the dairy. Some of them are in a laboratory where they test the milk to see that it is pure. Other men run the machinery through which the milk passes as it is prepared for us to drink. Then there are the men who clean the bottles and get them ready for the milk. Delivery men are also needed. They bring the milk to our door every day. We have two bottles left on our side porch every morning.

All of these workers are important. We could not have our milk without them. Now when I drink my milk for breakfast and dinner I think about all of these workers who helped to get our milk ready for us.

A "Thank-You" Prayer for Milk

Thank you, God, for milk which helps to keep me healthy and strong. Thank you for the cows and for the farmers who care for them. Thank you, too, for the dairymen who get the milk ready to drink, and for the delivery men who bring it to our door every day. Amen.

A Bible Verse to Remember

God . . . . giveth us richly all things to enjoy.
—1 Timothy 6:17b.

A Song of Spring Beauty

For the world which God has filled with beauty,
Oh give thanks unto the Lord,
For he is good.
For the bloom and fragrance of the flowers,
Oh give thanks unto the Lord,
For he is good.
For the greenness of the new grass and its softness under our feet,
Oh give thanks unto the Lord,
For he is good.
For the new leaves and the blossoms of the fruit trees,
Oh give thanks unto the Lord,
For he is good.
For the return of the birds and the cheerfulness of their songs,
Oh give thanks unto the Lord,
For he is good.
For the puffy white clouds against the blueness of the sky,
Oh give thanks unto the Lord,
For he is good.
For the sound of running water and the tapping of the rain,
Oh give thanks unto the Lord.
For he is good.
For all the beauties of God's world at Springtime,
Oh give thanks unto the Lord,
For he is good.

Farmer Friends

We went riding out in the country today. We saw farmers plowing in their fields. One of them was near the road when we drove by. Daddy waved at him, and he waved back.

"Who is that man, Daddy?" I asked.

"Just a farmer friend of mine," he said.

"But what is his name?"

"I do not know," Daddy answered.

"But you said he was your friend." I thought it was strange that Daddy did not know his friend's name.

"Yes, he is my friend. He is helping to raise the

food we eat. Helpers are friends even though we do not know their names," Daddy explained.

"Oh!" I said. I was beginning to understand. "We have lots of friends then, don't we?" I asked.

"Yes, and many of them we never see," Daddy replied.

Just then we passed another farm. A man was working in a field near the road. Daddy and I both waved, and he waved back.

"It is fun to have farmer friends, isn't it, Daddy?" I asked. And Daddy smiled at me as we drove on.

A "Thank-You" Prayer

Dear God, I am glad for friends who help us. Thank you for farmer friends. Thank you for the food they raise for us to eat. Help me to be friendly and helpful toward them, too. Amen.

A Bible Verse to Remember

A man that hath friends must show himself friendly.

—Proverbs 18:24a.

When the Robins Return

I saw a robin today. He was gayly flying around from one tree to another in our back yard. Mother said he was trying to find a place where he could build a nest.

We stood at the window and watched him. He flew over to a fork in one of the branches of the big pear tree. He turned this way and that and hopped about. He looked as if he might be measuring to see if a nest would fit in there.

"Will he build his nest there?" I asked.

Mother nodded her head.

Just then the bird flew away. But he was back soon bringing a lady robin with him. He showed her the spot he had chosen. It must have suited her, too, for they began to build their nest. One of them kept bringing pieces of twigs and thread and hair. The other one wove them into a nest, patting in some mud, too.

"How do they know just what to do?" I wanted to know.

"God has helped them know," Mother answered. "There may be tiny blue eggs in the nest later," she added. "And then baby robins from the eggs. That is part of God's plan and care for them, too."

"God knows how to care for everything, doesn't he?" I asked.

Mother just nodded and snuggled me closer in her arms.

A Prayer of Gladness

Dear God, I am glad that you thought about the birds when you planned the world. And that you planned how to care for them, too. I am glad for all the wise plans that you have made. Amen.

A Bible Verse to Remember

The Lord is good to all.

—Psalm 145:9a.

When I Forget

I went roller skating today. When I came in the house, I stopped in the kitchen to get a drink. Then I forgot to put my skates away where they belong. I left them on the kitchen floor where I had dropped them.

My brother Bob did not know I left my skates there. He went out to get a drink, too. He stepped on one of them. It began to roll, and he fell down.

I heard the noise, and then I heard him call,

"Who left these skates on the kitchen floor?"

Then I remembered. I was sorry I had forgotten. I went to the kitchen to get them. Bob was rubbing his knee.

"They are mine," I said. "I forgot to put them away."

"Don't you know it is dangerous to let them lie around like that?" Bob asked.

"Yes, and I am sorry. You did not hurt yourself, did you?"

"It is nothing serious," Bob said. "No bones were broken this time."

"I am glad," I told him. "I will try to remember to always put them away after this."

"That is a good idea," I heard Bob say as I started toward my room to put my skates away in the closet where they belong.

A Prayer for Help to Remember

I am sorry, God, when I forget and let my toys lie around after my play. Help me to remember to put them away so no one will fall over them and get hurt. Amen.

A Bible Verse to Remember

Follow . . . . . that which is good.

—3 John 11.

Making Gardens

Daddy and I made our gardens today. Daddy used a big fork and hoe and rake. I used a little hoe and rake. Mother bought them for me when we went downtown yesterday.

Daddy gave me some seeds for my garden. We planted lettuce and radish seeds. Breaking up the soft ground was fun. We dropped the seeds in rows. We raked the loose earth over them. The rows in Daddy's garden were long. The rows in my garden were short.

"What will make the seeds grow?" I asked.

Daddy said, "God planned the seeds in such a way that they have something inside of them that makes them grow.

He has planned for the rain and the sunshine, too. They will help the seeds to grow."

"Would they grow if they were not planted?" I wanted to know.

I was quite sure Daddy would say, "No," and he did.

"Then we are helping God, aren't we?" I asked.

"Yes," Daddy said. "We planted the seeds in the ground. So we are helping God to make them grow."

"I like helping God this way," I said.

A Prayer About Gardens

Dear God, our Father, I am glad for seeds to plant in our gardens. I am glad for the sunshine and the rain which will help them to grow. I like to help, too. Teach me to take care of my garden when it begins to grow. Amen.

Bible Verses to Remember

He maketh his sun to rise.

—Matthew 5:45.

He causeth to come down for you the rain.

—Joel 2:23.

A Mystery

A butterfly came out of our cocoon today. We found it in the woods last Fall.

At that time Mother had said, "Something wonderful is happening in this caterpillar's house. We may see a beautiful butterfly come out in the Spring."

Then she told me how a caterpillar had closed himself up in the cocoon by winding it around himself. And of the way he would change into a beautiful butterfly in the Spring.

We took the cocoon home and put it in a box. We have been watching it almost every day this Spring. But nothing happened until today a brown and yellow butterfly slowly crawled out of one end. It was all wet and sticky with its wings drooping.

We put the box in the sunlight for a while. Then we took it outdoors and put the butterfly on a branch of a bush. It kept opening and closing its wings as they dried in the sunlight. Suddenly it spread them wide and flew away.

"How can a caterpillar change into a butterfly?" I asked as we watched it go.

"I do not know," Mother softly answered.

"Does anybody know?" I asked.

"God knows, for he planned it that way," Mother said. "No one but God could have thought of sending beauty into the world like that."

A Prayer of Wonder

Dear God, it is wonderful to change a caterpillar into a butterfly. How does the caterpillar make the cocoon around itself? And what happens when it changes into a butterfly? I am glad that you know, God, and that you planned it that way. I love you more and more when I learn of these wonderful things. Amen.

A Bible Verse to Remember

He hath made everything beautiful in its time.
—Ecclesiastes 3:11.

One of God's Wonders

Today we found a tulip in bloom. We have been watching the buds for several days. This yellow one is the first one to open.

I helped mother put in the tulip bulbs last fall. It made me wonder now to see the yellow tulip holding its cup to the sun.

"What happened inside the bulb to make this flower?" I asked.

"We do not know," Mother told me. "Except that some bit of life inside began growing and growing until this flower unfolded."

"But the bulb was so dry and brown. How could it begin to grow?"

"It was only dry and brown on the outside. Inside was the life which God had planned."

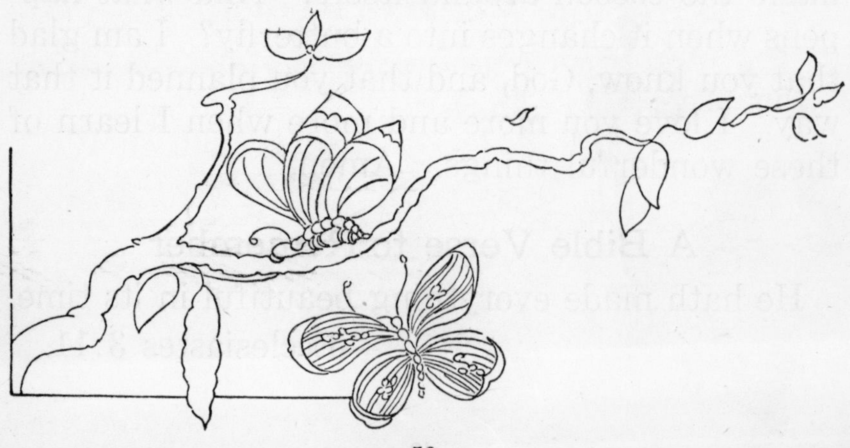

I looked at the yellow tulip again. "How could God think of such wonderful things?" I wondered.

"A man long ago wrote about the wonders of God. 'For thou art great, and doest wondrous things; thou art God alone,' he said. Perhaps that is the answer to your question."

"I guess he meant that only God could think of all of these things," I said when Mother had finished speaking.

"I am sure you are right," she answered with a smile.

A Prayer of Wonder

O, God, I wonder sometimes at all the things which you have made. Help me to understand your greatness. Help me always to remember that you used your greatness to put beauty and goodness into the world. Amen.

A Bible Verse to Remember

For thou art great, and doest wondrous things;
Thou art God alone.

—Psalm 86:10.

One of God's Promises

Our pear tree is full of blossoms. The buds at the top of the tree opened up first. Then the branches nearer the ground came into bloom. The white blossoms spread and spread until the whole tree was covered.

"What a pretty tree!" our neighbors said.

"Yes," Mother answered, "I do not believe it has ever been quite so pretty before."

I think it is pretty, too. Especially since the white petals are beginning to fall. A soft wind is blowing. It is shaking them off of the tree. Some of them fall under the tree. But some are carried farther away. They look like snow on the ground.

I scooped some up and put them in a basket. I took them in the house to Grandmother. She picked up a handful of blossoms and let them fall lightly through her fingers.

"These are God's promise of fruit on the tree," she told me. "They remind us that there will be pears on the tree in the Fall."

I liked the way Grandmother talked about the blossoms. No one had helped me think of them like that before.

A Prayer of Thanks

Thank you, God, for the blossoms on the trees in the Springtime. Help us to think of them as the promise of the fruit which will grow and be ripe in the Fall. Amen.

Bible Verses to Remember

And God said, Let the earth put forth . . . . fruit-trees bearing fruit of their kind. . . . And the earth brought forth . . . trees bearing fruit. . . . And God saw that it was good.

—Genesis 1:11, 12.

Long Evenings

It was still almost light when I came to bed tonight. I did not need a light at all. Mother says it is because the evenings are getting longer.

I like longer evenings. I like to lie in bed and hear all the night sounds. I can hear Mother and Daddy talking together out on the porch. Their voices sound low and far away. I can hear the crickets chirping in the grass. They make a cheerful, crackling sound. I can hear the leaves rustling outside my window. They make a shadow on my bedroom wall.

I like to watch the evening go. It will be darker soon. Then the stars will come out. The moon will come up, too. Sometimes I can see the stars from my window. Sometimes the moon makes a silver path across my room. I wonder if I will still be awake to see the stars tonight? And to see the silver path of the moon?

Evening-time like this makes me think of God. I like to talk with him before I go to sleep.

A Good-Night Prayer

Thank you, God, for the long evenings that go into nighttime. Thank you, too, for all the sounds

I hear when I am in bed. And for the stars that I see from my window. And the moon that makes a silver path across my room. Amen.

A Bible Verse to Remember

The day is thine, the night also is thine.

—Psalm 74:16a.

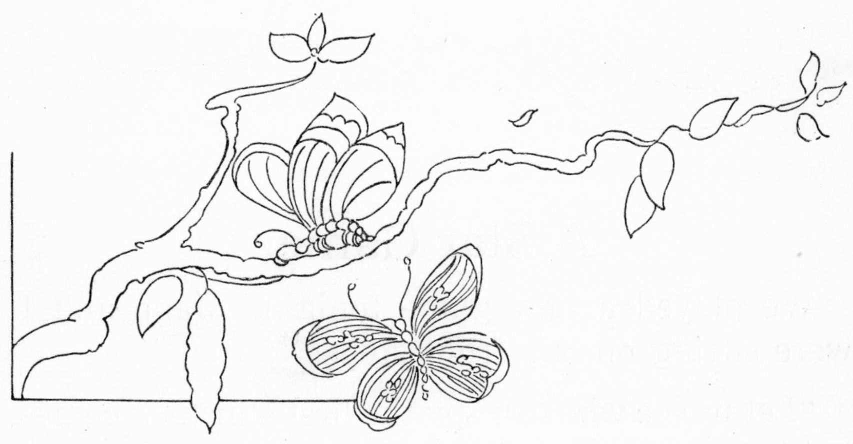

A Star Game

We played a new game tonight. Jane and I were sitting on our front steps.

"Let us see who can spy the first star as it comes out," Jane suggested.

"I see the moon," I said, looking up into the sky.

It was a new moon almost standing on tip-toe.

"Yes, I see the moon, too," Jane answered. "And a star," she added. "It just came out."

As we looked another star, and then another, and another shone in the sky. We counted ten of them. By that time they were breaking through the velvet curtain of the sky so quickly that we could not count them any more.

"I wonder how many there really are," I almost whispered as we watched together.

But Jane did not know. She only said, "Aren't you glad that God made the moon and the stars to brighten the sky at night?"

A Prayer of Wonder

When I look at all the stars, dear God, I wonder how you made them all. How are they fastened in the sky? And where do they get their light? I want to know more about them some day. Then I will know more about your wisdom, too. Amen.

Bible Verses to Remember

And God made the two great lights; the greater light to rule the day, and the lesser light to rule the night. He made the stars also. And God set them in the . . . . heaven to give light upon the earth. And God saw that it was good."

—Genesis 1:16, 17, 18b.

A New Pet

One of the hens on our farm has been missing for several weeks.

"She must have a nest of eggs hidden away," Daddy said. "She will come back when she hatches them out."

Daddy was right. Today the hen came strutting into the chicken yard. Nine yellow chicks were following her.

"Cluck, cluck, cluckity-cluck," she called to them.

"Peep, peep, peep-peep-peep," they answered.

I picked up one of the fluffy balls and held it in my hand. The mother hen began to scold. The little chicken tried to get free.

"Lie still," I said. "I will not hurt you."

Daddy watched me. "Would you like to have that little fellow for your own?" he asked.

"Oh, yes, may I?" I replied.

And Daddy said. "Fine. Then it is yours."

"You are mine," I said to the chick. "I will help to take care of you."

It stopped wiggling and lay quietly in my hand.

The mother hen stopped scolding, too. I wonder if she knew one of her baby chicks was my new pet.

A Prayer About Pets

Thank you, God, for pets. Help me to take care of mine as well as Mother helps you take care of me. Amen.

A Bible Verse to Remember

He careth for you.

—1 Peter 5:7.

A Broken Doll

I broke Mary's doll today. I did not mean to do it. It was an accident. She was playing house with Martha out under the tree in the side yard.

Teddy and I were playing ball in the yard, too. I guess we were too close to the girls. Once I batted the ball and it went to the side instead of forward. It hit Mary's doll and knocked it to the ground. The head broke in several pieces.

I ran to pick up the doll. But Mary was picking it up when I got there. I thought at first she was going to cry.

"I am sorry, Mary," I said. I tried to help her fit the pieces together. "Maybe Daddy can fix it. Or I can help to buy you another one," I added.

"I am sorry, too, but I know it was an accident." Mary tried to show me that she really did not care so much. "Thanks, but you need not get me another doll. Maybe we can have this fixed. I'll take it in the house now."

I watched Mary go. Somehow I did not want to play ball any more. Teddy did not want to play either. He picked up his bat and went home.

I kept thinking about Mary and her doll. I wished it were something of mine that had been broken. I wondered if I would be as forgiving about it as Mary was about her doll. It is sometimes hard for me to forgive.

A Prayer for Strength to Forgive

Dear God, I want to be forgiving. When something happens to hurt me, help me to forgive the person who does it. Amen.

A Bible Verse to Remember

Be ye kind one to another, tenderhearted, forgiving each other.

—Ephesians 4:32a.

A Sick Neighbor

Our neighbor is sick. She lives all alone in the house next door. She has been sick for a week now.

Miss Wilson works out in her yard a lot. Mother missed her one day. She did not see her outside at all. So she went over to see what was the matter. Since then, Mother has been going over several times every day. She stayed with Miss Wilson several nights, too.

Mother also fixes food for Miss Wilson to eat. I took her dinner over to her today. We decorated the tray with some flowers from her own garden. She liked that.

Miss Wilson has been worrying about her garden. She said that it will not grow unless she gets better soon and can take care of it. Daddy told her not to think about her yard and garden at all. He would take care of it for her.

Daddy mowed the grass last night. Bob helped trim it around the walks. I helped rake it up. Daddy and Bob are going to weed the garden tonight. I can help them with that, too.

I am sorry Miss Wilson is sick. I am glad that we can help her, though. Helping a neighbor is fun.

A Prayer About Neighbors

Thank you, God, for neighbors. Help us to be kind and helpful to those who live near to us. Amen.

A Bible Verse to Remember

They help every one his neighbor.

—Isaiah 41:6.

A Song of Gladness

I am glad for my eyes so that I can see the color of my mother's dress, our baby's face, and the bubbling of the water fountain.

I will give thanks unto God,
For I am wonderfully made.

I am glad for my ears so that I can hear the bark of my dog, my father's laugh, and the crackling of burning leaves.

I will give thanks unto God,
For I am wonderfully made.

I am glad for my voice so that I can talk, and sing, and whistle, and just make joyful noises.

I will give thanks unto God,
For I am wonderfully made.

I am glad for my legs and feet so that I can walk, and run, and ride my scooter.

I will give thanks unto God,
For I am wonderfully made.

I am glad for my arms and hands and fingers so that I can reach, and hold, and feel the softness of the blanket on my bed.

I will give thanks unto God,
For I am wonderfully made.

I am glad for my mind which helps me to think, and for that part of me with which I love.

I will give thanks unto God,
For I am wonderfully made.

A "Thank You" for Mother

I can hear the humming of the washing machine in the basement. Mother is washing our clothes. Some of them are already done. They are hanging out on the line in the sunshine to dry. They are so clean and white. The wind is flapping the sheets and towels back and forth. It is puffing out my dresses. They look funny almost standing up that way.

Mother got up early to begin her washing. Billy and I were still in bed. I guess all mothers have to get up early to take care of their families. There is always so much to do. Tomorrow Mother will need to iron the clothes and put them away. Some of them will need mending. There will be buttons that must be sewed on, too. I wonder why I have never thought about this before.

Mother will be tired when she gets all the clothes hung up. I think I will surprise her and wash the breakfast dishes. Maybe Billy will help me. I can pick up the Sunday paper in the living room, too. Then I shall look for other things to do. I want to help all I can. I can tell Mother "thank you" for all she does to take care of me by helping like this in every way that I can.

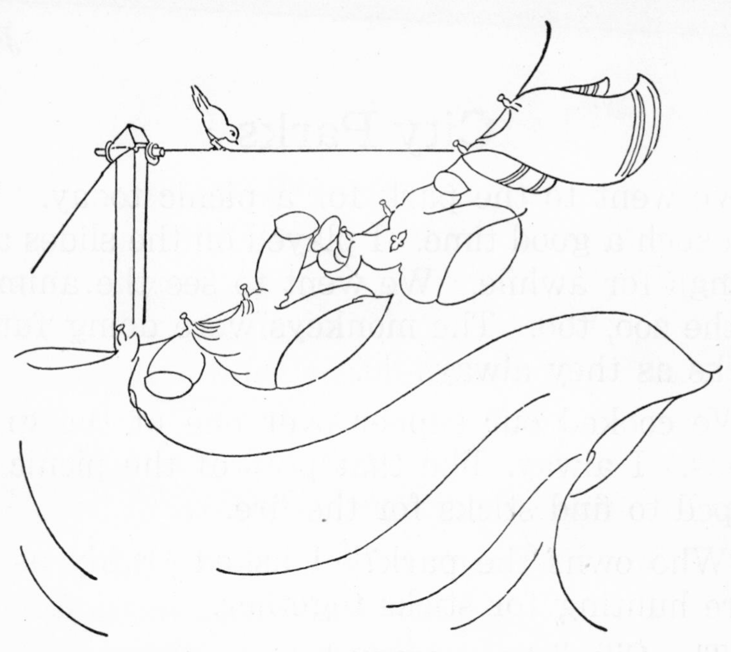

A Prayer for Help to Remember

Dear Father, God, help me always to remember the ways in which my mother loves and takes care of me. Help me to be careful not to make any more work for her than is necessary. And, God, help me to remember to show that I love her by helping her in every way that I can. Amen.

A Bible Verse to Remember

By love serve one another.

—Galatians 5:13c.

City Parks

We went to the park for a picnic today. We had such a good time. I played on the slides and swings for awhile. We went to see the animals in the zoo, too. The monkeys were doing funny tricks as they always do.

We cooked our supper over one of the grate ovens. I always like that part of the picnic. I helped to find sticks for the fire.

"Who owns the park?" I asked Daddy as we were hunting for sticks together.

"The City," he answered.

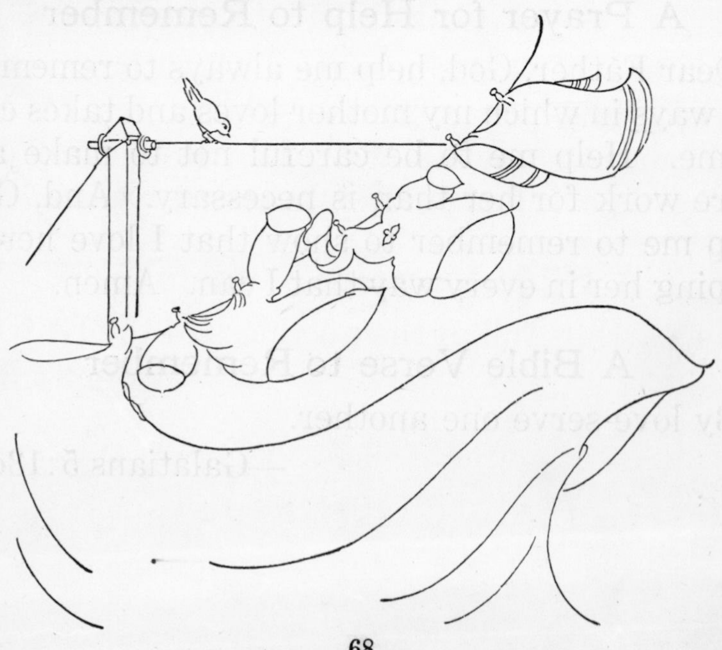

"Does the City put up the swings and slides and take care of the zoo?" I wanted to know.

"Yes," Daddy answered again.

"But who pays for all of that?"

"Those of us who own houses or land in the City pay taxes. Part of that money is used to keep up our parks. Then everyone can enjoy them," Daddy answered.

I thought about that for a minute. I thought about the boys and girls who do not have any other place in which to play.

"I am glad that we have parks for children who do not have any other playgrounds," I said.

A "Thank-You" Prayer

Thank you, God, for parks with playgrounds and zoos and picnic places. Thank you for the good times we have in our park. Help every city to have a park for children to enjoy. Amen.

A Bible Verse to Remember

The earth is full of the goodness of the Lord.
—Psalm 33:5.

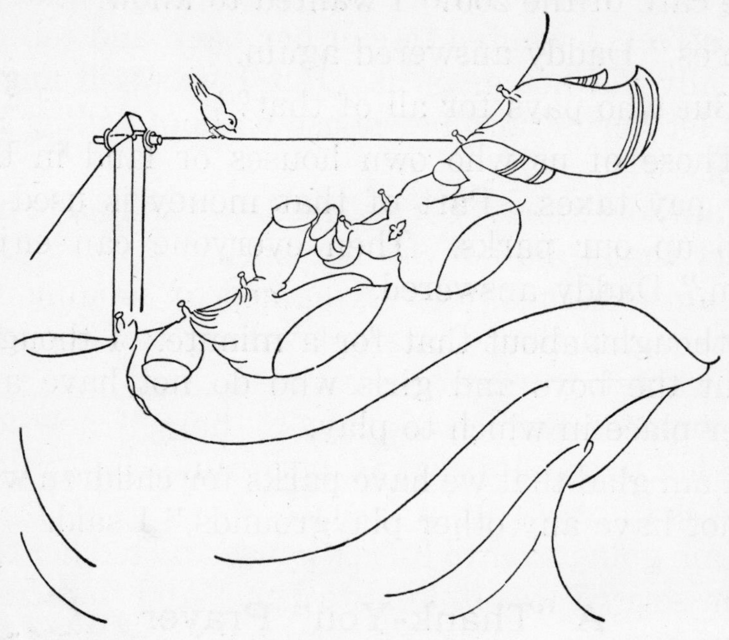

A Quarrel

Ruth came over to play with me this afternoon. She brought her doll with her. We played together for a long time. Then I got tired playing dolls. I wanted Ruth to play store with me, but she still wanted to play house.

"I am your company," she said. "And because I am your company, you should do what I want to do."

Then I became angry. "I am tired of having company," I told her. "You can take your doll and go home and play by yourself."

Ruth looked surprised. She picked up her doll and left. I watched her go. When she got across the street, I wanted to call her back and tell her I really did not mean it. But I was still angry, so I let her go into her house without calling her back.

I am sorry now. Sorry that I was unkind to her. Sorry that I did not call her back.

I am ashamed, too. Ashamed of sending her home. And that I was not willing to play what she wanted to play.

I suppose Ruth is playing by herself now as I told her to do. It is not as much fun playing alone as it is to play with a friend.

I am going over to Ruth's house and tell her that I am sorry I was unkind to her. And that I still want her for my friend, and will play what she wants to play.

A Prayer for Strength

Dear God, it is hard to say "I am sorry" when I have been unkind to a friend. Or when I have wanted my own way. Make me strong enough to say that I have done wrong, and to ask my friends to forgive me. Help me always to try to be kind and friendly even when I do not feel like it. Amen.

A Bible Verse to Remember

Be at peace one with another.

—Mark 9:50.

Airplanes

Uncle Tom took us out to the airport this morning. We went in time to see one of the big planes come in.

"Look, there she comes," Uncle Tom said when the plane was still a long way off. "You can hear her motors running smoothly."

We watched the plane come nearer and nearer. She flew above the landing field and then came slowly down. Her wheels hit the ground, and the pilot taxied her around to the waiting platform.

Some passengers got off. The mail and luggage were unloaded. The gasoline man filled up the tank. Another man inspected the wheels and wings. It was not long until the plane was ready to fly again.

The new passengers got on. Their luggage and some mail were loaded into the plane. The propeller began to whirl and whirl. The pilot got in and began to tune up the motor. The plane started slowly across the landing field. When it got almost to the other end it began to rise from the ground. It went higher and higher and on and on until it was just a shiny speck in the sky.

I like to watch the airplanes come and go like that. I want to fly in one of them when I grow older. Maybe I will be a pilot and carry mail and passengers, too.

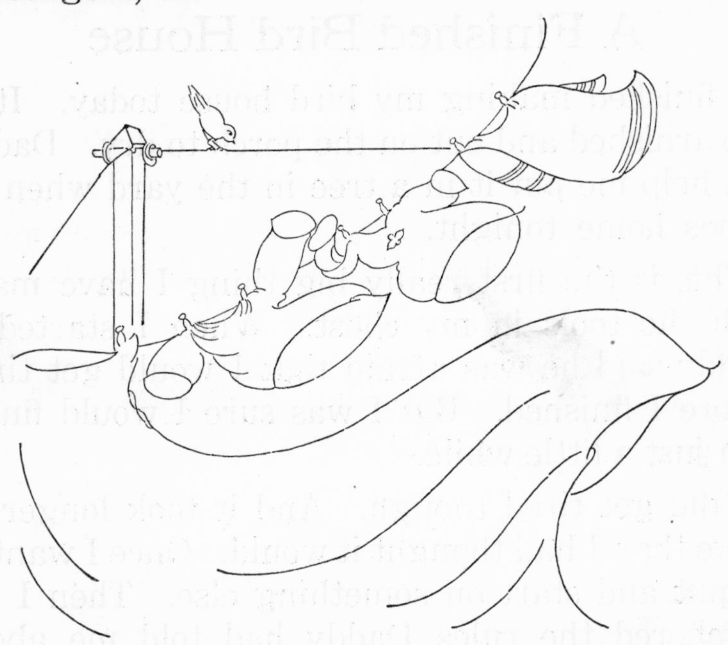

A Prayer of Joy and Sorrow

Dear God, I am glad that men have learned to make planes to fly in the air. Keep the pilots and passengers safe from danger. I am sorry, God, that some planes are used to carry bombs that are dropped to kill people and to wreck their homes and other buildings. Help men to use airplanes only to do good. Amen.

A Bible Verse to Remember

Let us love one another.

—1 John 4:7a.

A Finished Bird House

I finished making my bird house today. It is all varnished and out on the porch to dry. Daddy will help me put it in a tree in the yard when he comes home tonight.

This is the first really big thing I have made with the tools in my chest. When I started it Daddy said he was afraid that I would get tired before I finished. But I was sure I would finish it in just a little while.

I did get tired though. And it took longer to make than I had thought it would. Once I wanted to quit and start on something else. Then I remembered the rules Daddy had told me about when I got my tools.

"A good carpenter," he had said, "follows several rules. One is that he always plans his work well and does his best. Another is that he always finishes one piece of work before he begins another one."

I wanted to be a good carpenter, so I kept right on working. I am glad now that I did. It was easier to finish my bird house after I had remembered the rules.

Daddy will be glad to know that it is done. I wonder what he will say when he sees it.

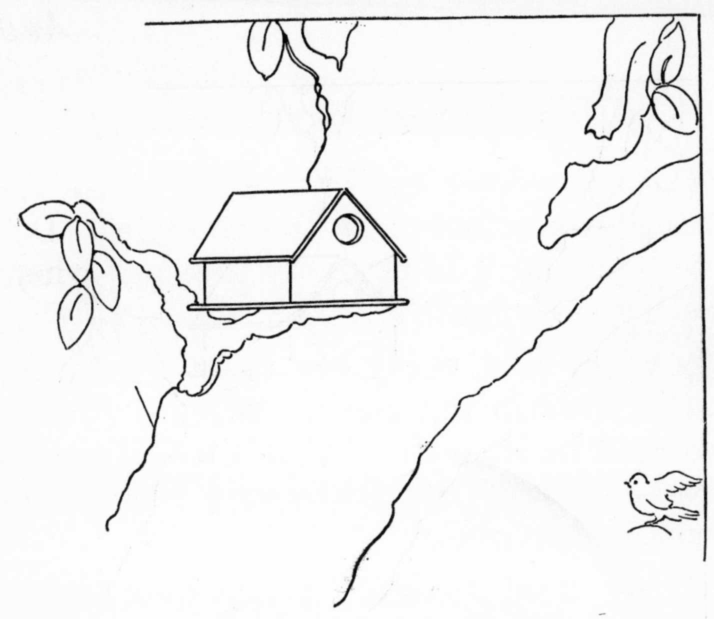

A Prayer for Help

I like to make things with my hands, God. Things out of wood that I can saw and hammer and nail. Sometimes it is hard to finish making the things I begin. Help me to learn to finish one piece of work before I start making another. Amen.

A Bible Verse to Remember

Whatsoever thy hand findeth to do, do it with thy might.

—Ecclesiastes 9:10.

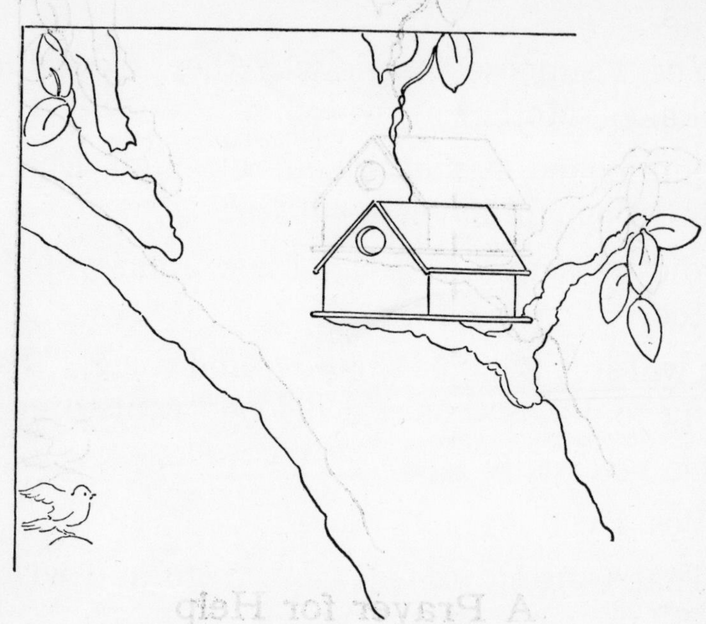

Aunt Jane's Letter

We got a letter from Aunt Jane this morning. She and Uncle Jack and Ralph are going on a vacation. She asked Mother if either John or I could go with them. They can take only one of us because their cabin is a small one. Next year, she said, the other one of us could go.

Mother talked with Daddy about it first. They said one of us could go, and that we should decide who it would be.

"Will there be fishing and swimming and perhaps a row boat?" John asked. He is two years older than I am. So he knows more about those things.

"Yes, I suppose that is why they are going to the Lake," Mother answered.

John looked at me. "You better go, Don," he said. "You will have lots of fun."

I did want to go. But I knew John wanted to go, too.

"I will stay at home this year and you go," I said, trying to act as though I did not want to go.

"Do you really mean it?" John asked.

"Yes, I will go next year."

"That's grand of you. I will go and write to Aunt Jane right away."

Seeing how happy John was made me glad that I said I would stay at home.

A Prayer for Strength

Dear God, make me strong enough to be unselfish. Help me to be willing to give up something that I want for myself so that someone else may enjoy it. Help me to be glad when I can make other people happy in that way. Amen.

A Bible Verse to Remember

Trust in the Lord, and do good.

—Psalm 37:3a.

Plans for a Visitor

Aunt Lucy is coming to visit us. Mother and Jane and I cleaned up the guest room for her. I picked some flowers out of our garden for her. I put them in a bowl on the dresser in her room. I hung some yellow towels in the bathroom for her, too. It has been fun getting ready.

Now we are all ready to go to meet her. Daddy is going to drive us to the depot in the car. We are waiting for him to come after us. It is almost time now.

"I guess everything is ready," Mother said.

"Oh, I almost forgot," Jane thought of something else. "That new book of poems. I thought maybe Aunt Lucy might like to read that. I'll go and put it on the table in her room."

Daddy drove up just as Jane came back. We talked of Aunt Lucy as we drove down to meet her.

"I wish Aunt Lucy would stay all summer," I told them.

"We know she cannot do that," Mother answered. "We will make her visit as pleasant as we can, and then she will want to come back."

"We must plan some picnics," Jane said. "Aunt Lucy likes picnics."

"Let me help plan something for her, too. May I, Mother?" I asked.

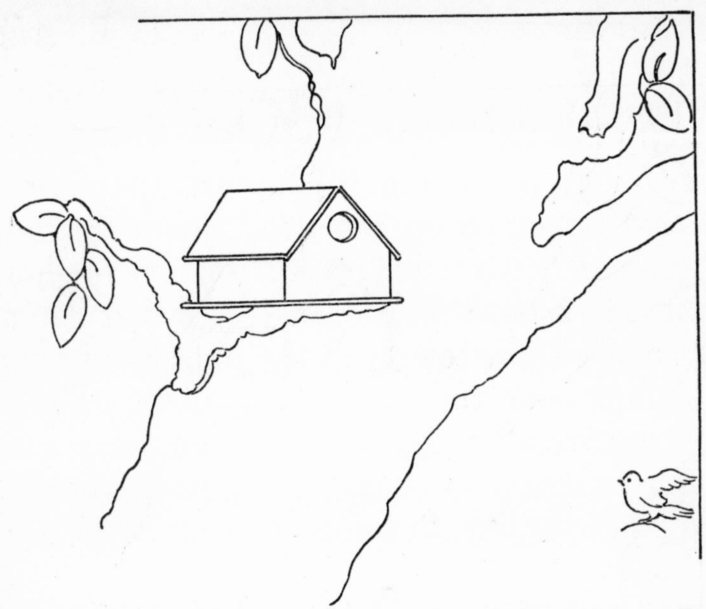

"Of course, you may help," was her answer. "This whole family will work together to make Aunt Lucy's visit a happy one."

A Prayer of Happiness

I am happy, God, when we have visitors in our home. It is fun to help get ready for them. And to plan together for ways to make them happy. Help me to do my part when visitors come. Help us all to make our home the kind that people like to visit. Amen.

A Bible Verse to Remember

Our help is in the . . . Lord,
Who made heaven and earth.

—Psalm 124:8.

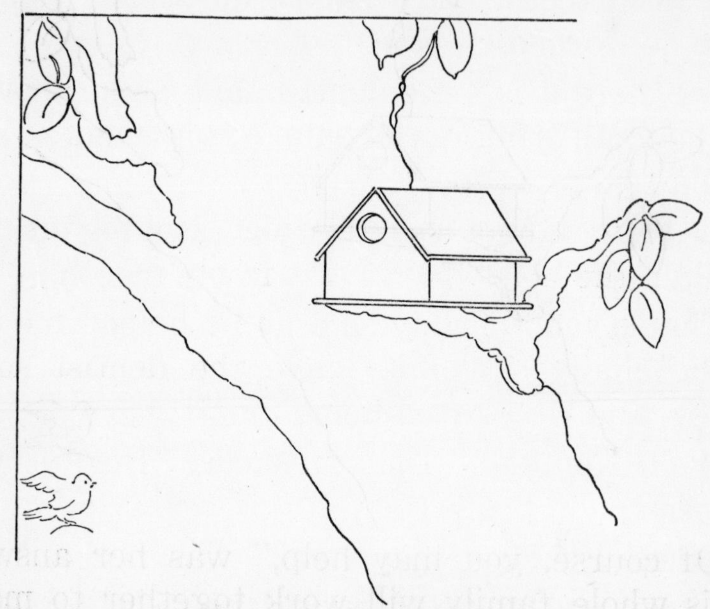

A New Friend

I had a tooth pulled today. Daddy took me to see the dentist. I sat in the dentist's chair. He pumped me up high so he could look in my mouth. He fastened a clean towel around my neck. He washed his hands and then moved my tooth back and forth with his finger.

"That is one of your baby teeth," he said. "We will pull it out so your second tooth below it will come in straight."

I sat very still while he got his pincers and pulled out the tooth. It came out easily. I was not a bit afraid. You see Daddy had told me that the dentist is our friend, and that he wants to help us have good teeth. So I sat as quietly as I could while he worked.

"See, here it is," the dentist said, as he showed me the tooth lying in the palm of his hand. "You were a real man, too."

The tooth did not look very big. Not big enough to fill up the hole which I felt in my mouth.

"Thank you," Daddy said as he helped me out of the chair. Then he gave the dentist some money, and we started home.

"Well, Kenneth," Daddy asked. "How do you like your new friend?"

"Fine," I said.

"I knew you would. You will meet other friends who will help you in other ways," Daddy replied.

A "To-Be-Helpful" Prayer

I am glad, God, for the dentist friend who helps to take care of my teeth. Thank you, God, for all the friends who help us. I want to be a kind, helping friend to boys and girls when I grow to be big. I want to be helpful now, too. Amen.

A Bible Verse to Remember

That which maketh a friend to be desired is his kindness.

—Proverbs 19:22.

Thoughts in Church

I like to come to church sometimes with my father and mother. It is so quiet here. Only the organ is playing now. I like to hear the organ. It makes me feel quiet and rested inside.

I like the singing of the hymns, too. I can read some of the words. Mother always holds her book low so I can see them. I feel as if I am a part of the church when I sing with the other people.

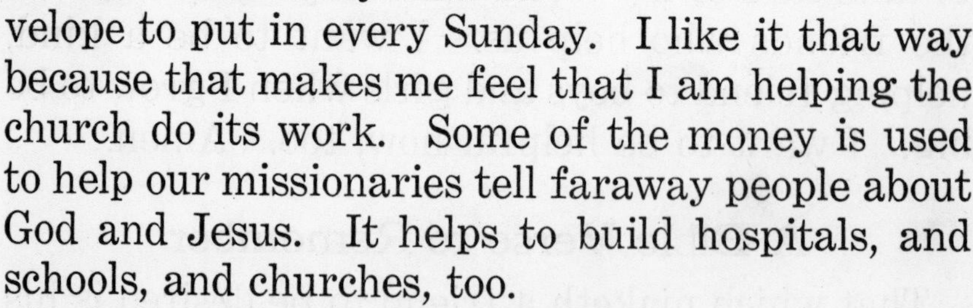

I can take part in the offering. I have my own envelope to put in every Sunday. I like it that way because that makes me feel that I am helping the church do its work. Some of the money is used to help our missionaries tell faraway people about God and Jesus. It helps to build hospitals, and schools, and churches, too.

Now the preacher is talking. I like to watch him. I do not always understand what he is saying, but I can understand the stories he tells. I shall ask Mother and Daddy about the things I do not understand.

The church is most quiet during the prayer time. Just as if everybody is ready to talk with God then. I sometimes say my own prayer. Maybe other people do, too. I am sure that God can hear all of them. He seems to be so very near to us all.

A "Thank-You" Prayer

Dear God, thank you for my church. I am glad that I have a church where I can go to learn more about you and your world. I am glad, too, that I can help my church do its work by giving my offerings. Amen.

A Bible Verse to Remember

My house shall be called a house of prayer for all people.

—Isaiah 56:7.

A Broken Window

It is sometimes hard for me to do right. Especially when other boys laugh at me because I want to do what I think is right.

It was hard like that today. I was playing ball with some boys on the corner lot. We were having a good time until we broke a window in the basement of the house next door.

The boys began to run away.

"Aren't you going to tell?" I asked Charles, who had come back after his bat.

"Tell? What for?" he asked. "No one saw us do it. Come on, let's get away from here."

"But that is not right," I told him.

Charles laughed at me, and then ran on and left me alone. The boys waited at the end of the block to see what I was going to do.

I looked toward the house with the broken window. Charles was right that no one had seen us break it. The people living in the house did not know about it either. I wanted to tell them, but I did not like to have the boys laughing at me. I went home and told Mother what had happened.

"You were right," she said, "in wanting to tell.

I know the lady who lives there. We will talk with her over the telephone and you can tell her what happened."

I was glad I had told Mother. I felt better about it after I had told, too.

A Prayer for Courage

There are times, God, when it is hard for me to do right. Give me courage to be honest even when other people laugh at me. Amen.

A Bible Verse to Remember

Do that which is right and good in the sight of the Lord.

—Deuteronomy 6:18.

Our School Safety Patrol

My brother Tom has been elected as a member of our school Safety Patrol. He has been assigned to a corner a block from the school building. Today was his first day to help us cross the street. He was very careful to see that none of us got hurt. He watched the traffic lights. When they were red, he made us wait until they changed. When they were green, he gave the signal for us to cross the street. He was also careful to see that we did not cross when the lights were changing from one color to the other.

After he helped us across today, I stood and watched Tom for a while. I like the way he looked with his new white belt across his shoulder and around his waist. His badge was all shiny in the sun, too. He looked very important as he worked. I am sure he knew I was watching him, but he did not pay any attention to me. He kept on looking for the cars and the changing of the lights. He was helping some more children cross the street when I went in to school.

Tom is only one of the boys on our school Safety Patrol. But I am glad that he was chosen. I am sure he will do his work well. I will help him by watching the traffic lights too.

A Prayer for Help

Dear God, I am glad for our school Safety Patrol. Make the members strong to keep all the rules of the patrol helpers. I want to help them, God. Teach me to wait patiently when the light is red and to watch for their signals. Help me to obey them cheerfully. Amen.

A Bible Verse to Remember

Have the same care one for another.

1 Corinthians 12:25b.

Taking Turns at Play

Jack was hurt today at recess. It happened while we were playing on the slide. Miss Wilson, our teacher, said it was because we crowded too much and did not wait for our turn. We did not wait until Jack was at the bottom of the slide before some of the rest of us got on. We knocked him down and fell on top of him because we did not give him time to get out of the way before we came down.

Jack was not badly hurt. He only skinned his knees. Miss Wilson washed them and put some kind of medicine and patches on them. She told us that Jack might have been really hurt. That he might have broken his arm or leg. She was glad that he was only scratched. We were glad, too.

After the accident we were careful to take turns on the slide. We lined up in a row and waited until the one in front of us was out of the way before we slid down. No one got hurt when we played that way. Everybody had lots of turns and fun, too. I guess Miss Wilson was right about taking turns being the happiest way to play.

A Prayer for Help

Wherever I play, God, help me to remember to take turns. Keep me from pushing and causing accidents. Thank you for playgrounds, and slides, and swings, and things used for playing. Amen.

A Bible Verse to Remember

The Lord is my helper.

—Hebrews 13:6a.

A Song of Thanksgiving

I thank you, God, for the red, and the brown, and the gold, and the yellow colors of the Autumn season.

Praise the Lord for his lovingkindness,
And for his wonderful works to the children of men.

I thank you, God, for the smell of burning bonfires, and for the crackling of the twigs and the leaves.

Praise the Lord for his lovingkindness,
And for his wonderful works to the children of men.

I thank you, God, for the ripened corn, and the pumpkins, and the potatoes in the fields.

Praise the Lord for his lovingkindness,
And for his wonderful works to the children of men.

I thank you, God, for the nuts and the apples which are gathered for our Winter use.

Praise the Lord for his lovingkindness,
And for his wonderful works to the children of men.

I thank you, God, for men and women and boys and girls who help to harvest these foods for us.

Praise the Lord for his lovingkindness,
And for his wonderful works to the children of men.

Wool for Clothing

Mother is knitting me a new sweater. It will be a green sweater. One that buttons down the front. I like to hear the "click-click-click" of her needles. I like to watch her come to the end of one row and then start back again. Soon that row is finished, too.

"Where did the yarn come from?" I asked her today.

"From the wool which covers the sheep's back," she said. "You remember the sheep we saw in the country yesterday? This yarn was made from wooly coats like theirs."

"Does it hurt the sheep to have their wool cut off?" I wanted to know.

"Not unless the shears slip and clip their skin," Mother told me. "Cutting their wool in the Spring is being kind to the sheep. They are hot and uncomfortable with their heavy covering just as you are hot and uncomfortable in your Winter snow suit in warmer weather."

"And does their wool grow out again?" was my next question.

"Yes," Mother answered. "And then it is clipped again the next Spring. It is put into bags and sold to the wool merchant. Later it is made

into yarns and woolen cloth. That is one of the ways God has planned for us to have clothing."

A "Thank-You" Prayer

Thank you, God, for the wool that comes from the sheep's back. Help the men who cut it to be careful not to hurt the sheep. Let their wool grow thick again so they will be warm when Winter comes. Amen.

A Bible Verse to Remember

The Lord hath done great things for us,
Whereof we are glad.

—Psalm 126:3.

Autumn Leaves

The leaves on the trees are changing their color. Some of them are golden. Some are orange. Some are flame colored. And some of them are two or three colors. Green and yellow. Or green and yellow and red.

I like the leaves colored this way. I picked up some of the prettiest ones as I came home from school. There were so many it was hard for me to choose. I kept picking them up until soon I had more than I could carry.

I wonder what makes them change their color like that. Someone said it was the frost in the air.

I guess God thought about changing the color of the leaves in the Fall when he planned for trees.

He planned for such wonderful things to happen! I do not know which is more wonderful—the leaves coming out green in the Spring, or turning to yellows and browns and reds in the Fall. Last Spring I thought that Springtime was more wonderful. But I feel differently about it now.

I am sure that God likes the trees when they are colored this way. He would not have thought of so much beauty if he did not enjoy it too.

A Prayer of Wonder

I wonder, God, at all the color you have put into the world for us to enjoy. What makes the leaves change their color in the Fall? Thank you, God, for planning for the Autumn in this way. Amen.

A Bible Verse to Remember

Thou crownest the year with Thy goodness.

—Psalm 65:11a.

Reading Time

Mother read to us again tonight before we went to bed. We sat in the big chair by the table. That chair always holds Mother and Sally and me. We know just how to sit in it so there is room for all three of us. It was especially comfortable tonight. And the story was interesting, too.

Sally is too little to understand the story. She just looks at the pictures. She likes to hear Mother read though. So do I. She reads so quiet-like. Then sometimes she makes the people in the story talk. Sally laughs at that, and I laugh, too. We are always sorry when the story is done.

Sometimes there is time to read the story through again. Tonight there was time to hear it still another time. I said some of the parts with Mother that time. Like the noises which the wind makes as it talks to the trees. Or the sound of people walking or climbing up the stairs. I like to read with Mother that way. Then I can tell the story alone to Sally some other time when Mother is too busy to read to us.

I am glad that Mother reads like this before bedtime. I told her "thank you for the story" when she turned out the light after we were in bed. Sally said "thank you," too.

A Prayer of Thanks for Mother

Thank you, God, for my mother. And for everything she does for us. I am glad for the times she plays with us. I am glad for the times she reads to us. I like to hear her nice, soft voice. Amen.

A Bible Verse to Remember

It is a good thing to give thanks unto the Lord.
—Psalm 92:1a.

A New Snow Suit

I got a new snow suit today. It was fun shopping with Mother. We went to the children's department of a big store. They had lots of snow suits. Blue ones, brown ones, red ones, and plaid ones. We got a dark blue one. It is size nine. I am only eight years old, but Mother said I can wear it again next year when I will be nine. My old suit is too little. I am glad this is a bigger one.

"Do you know who paid for your snow suit?" Mother asked me as we were going home. I was carrying the box, myself.

"You did," I answered.

"Yes, I paid for it now," Mother smiled. "But where did Mother get the money?"

"Daddy gave it to you," I said.

"Yes," Mother answered. "And Daddy worked hard to earn the money. Daddy works every day so that we can have clothes to wear and food to eat."

"And does he work so that we can have a home, too?" I asked.

"Yes. Daddy is happy to work for us in this way. He is helping God take care of us."

"Oh," I said. . . .

When Daddy comes home tonight, I am going to thank him for my new snow suit, for our home, and for everything he does for us.

A Prayer of Thanks for Daddy

Dear God, thank you for my Daddy. And for the way in which he helps you take care of us. Make me always thankful for my home, my clothes, and everything that he does for me. Amen.

A Bible Verse to Remember

Honor thy father and thy mother.

—Exodus 20:12a.

Birthdays

Today was Mother's birthday. Daddy bought a new purse for her. Jane gave her a new blouse. Tom chose a book for his present. Mine was a "Do Not Forget" pad I made for her at school.

We wrapped the gifts in tissue paper. We tied them with different colored ribbons. We put fancy bows and stickers on them, too.

Mother did not know about them until at breakfast this morning. You see we put them at her place at the table then. I got up early and helped set the table. I arranged her packages, too.

When Mother came in from the kitchen, we all

said together, "Happy Birthday." Then we sang the birthday song for her.

Mother was surprised. She opened her gifts before we ate our breakfast. She liked her new purse. She liked her new blouse. She liked Tom's book. And she liked my "Do Not Forget" pad, too. She smiled as she said "Thanks" to all of us.

Mother was very happy. The rest of us were happy, too. I guess it must have been because we were celebrating Mother's birthday. We all decided that birthdays were fun, but that Mother's birthday was the most fun of all.

A "Thank-You" Prayer for Birthdays

Thank you, God, for birthdays, and for other people's birthdays. May everybody always be happy on their birthday. Make me always glad to give gifts to others. Amen.

A Bible Verse to Remember

It is more blessed to give than to receive.

—Acts 20:35c.

A Lost Dog

My dog is lost. His name was Pal. He was home when I went to school this afternoon. He was playing in the yard when Mother went downtown. But he was gone when she got back.

Jerry, who lives across the street, helped us look for him. Mother called and called, but Pal did not come. Jerry and I went all over the neighborhood looking for him, but we did not find him. No one had even remembered seeing Pal this afternoon.

When Daddy came home, he helped us look for my dog. He went in the car to the park and places where we have taken Pal. But he did not find him either. He called the police station to see if someone had found him and taken him there. But the men there had not heard anything about a lost dog.

I am sure Pal was not hit by a car. He is too careful to get hit. Nobody had seen an accident of that kind, either. Daddy thinks maybe he followed someone away. Or that he was picked up and taken out of town. If that is what happened, I hope he will have a good home. And that his new owner will be kind to him.

It is nighttime now. Mother and I called for Pal again. But he did not answer. Daddy said he would let him in if he scratches on the door tonight. He will call me and let me know, too.

A Prayer for Courage

Dear God, I thank you for my pet. Help me to be brave if something should happen to him. Make me kind in my care for him. Amen.

A Bible Verse to Remember

The Lord is nigh unto all them that call upon him.

—Psalm 145:18.

Work for Everyone

Jimmy was not at school this week. Miss Mason said he did not come because he did not have warm clothes to wear. His father does not have work to do, and Jimmy's clothes are about worn out.

Miss Mason asked us if we had a suit or sweater or pair of shoes we would like to give to Jimmy.

I told Mother and Daddy about it. Mother called Miss Mason. She said she would go to see Jimmy's mother. We are going to give him one of my pair of slacks and a sweater. I helped Mother decide which ones. We picked out some dark red slacks and a striped sweater. They are

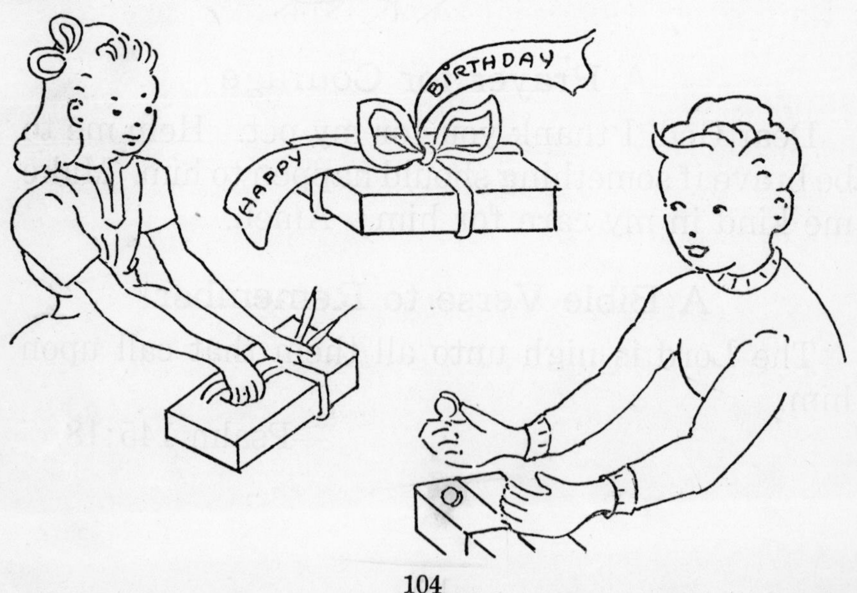

almost new. I have worn them only a few times. I will have to be more careful with my others now because I will not have this pair to wear.

Daddy says it is fine to give the slacks and sweater to Jimmy. But he says that Jimmy's father needs work so he can care for his family. When Mother goes to visit at Jimmy's house, she will find out what kind of work his father does. Then Daddy will see what he can do about getting him a job. He heard the manager say they needed more men in the shop where he works. Maybe Jimmy's father can work there with him. Then he can buy clothes for his family. And Jimmy can come to school again.

A Prayer for Work

I am sorry, God, that some fathers do not have work to do. Make us willing to share with their families until they can take care of them. Help the workers to plan so that everyone will have work to do so they can keep their families happy and well. Amen.

A Bible Verse to Remember

Let us work that which is good toward all men.
—Galatians 6:10.

A Kind Friend

I got lost today. I went downtown with Mother and we got separated in a crowded store. I tried to find her, but I could not see her any place. Then I tried to remember what she had told me to do if I ever got lost. But I became frightened and began to cry.

A lady in the store stopped to ask me what was the matter. I told her I was lost. She said she would wait with me at the door and we would see my mother when she went out to look for me. She sounded so sure we would find her, that I felt better.

But we waited and waited, and Mother did not come. "Do you think she has gone home without me?" I asked my new friend.

"Oh, no, she would not do that," she told me. "Come, we will go to the office and see if she has been there asking about you."

But just then I saw Mother coming quickly toward us. I was glad to see her. She was glad to see me, too.

"Oh, there you are," she cried. "How glad I am that I have found you."

Mother thanked the lady who had been so kind to me. I thanked her, too. I would like to have her for my friend.

A "To-Be-Friendly" Prayer

I am glad, God, for kind friends who help me when I need them. They make me think of you, because you are kind and helpful. Thank you for these friends. Make me always ready to be friendly in helpful ways, too. Amen.

A Bible Verse to Remember

Ye are my friends if ye do the things which I command you.

—John 15:14.

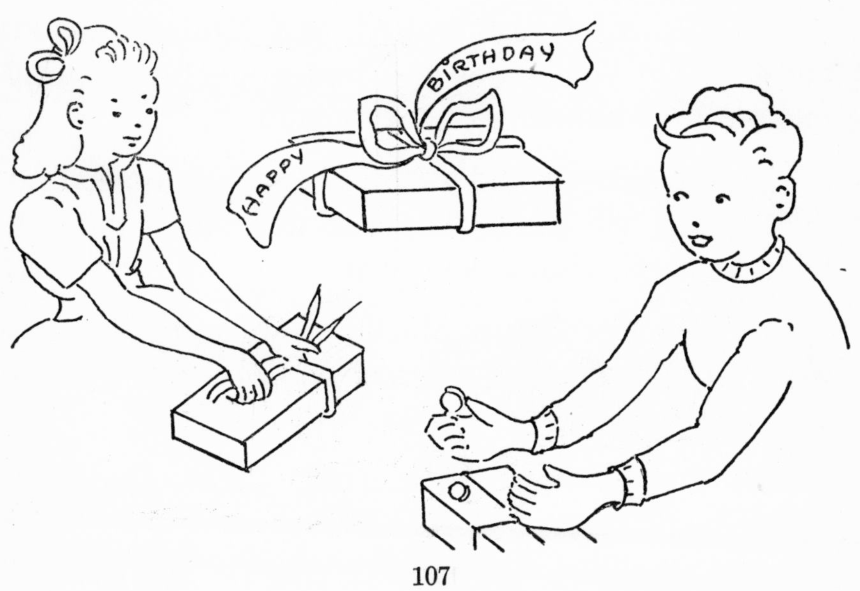

Winter Beauty

"We had a heavy snow last night," Daddy said at breakfast this morning. "I wonder how many beautiful sights we can find in God's world today."

"What do you mean, Daddy?" I asked.

"Oh, lovely scenes like that clump of bushes across the street all covered with snow. And like those. . . ."

"Wait, Daddy," Mother interrupted. "Don't find them all. Let us make a game of it. Let us each one look about us today for these bits of winter beauty. Then tonight at the supper table, we will tell what we have found."

"Oh, yes, that will be fun," Jean said excitedly.

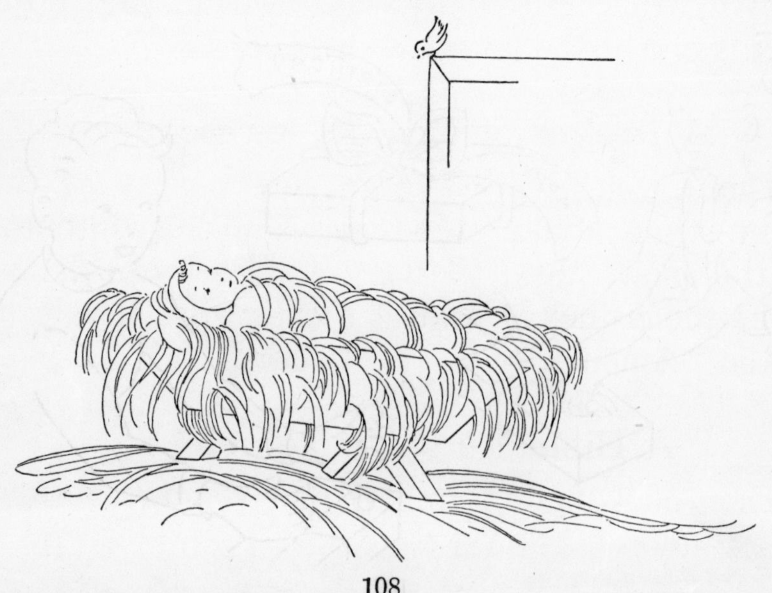

"All right," Daddy laughed. "I will save what I was going to say until this evening."

I kept watching all day long for beautiful things to tell about. So did Mother and Daddy and Jean.

Everyone was ready when Daddy said tonight, "Well, what did you see that was beautiful today?"

"The sun sparkling on the snow-covered branches of the trees," Jean said.

"And the icicles glistening in the sunlight," Mother added.

"The star tracks which the birds left behind them in the snow." I took my turn.

"I was going to say this morning, the layer of snow on the telephone wires," Daddy said, "but the wind has blown it all off today."

"We will count it anyway," we all said, "for that is one of the loveliest sights of all."

A Prayer of Thanks for Beauty

Thank you, dear God, for the beauty of the Wintertime. I like the softness and the whiteness of the snow. And the way it piles up in drifts. I like the crunchy sound it makes when I walk in it, too. Amen.

A Bible Verse to Remember

Thou hast made Summer and Winter.

—Psalm 74:17b.

Growing in Wisdom

I stayed after school today to help Miss Jenkins clean off the blackboards.

"Where did you learn to teach?" I asked Miss Jenkins.

"I went to college and learned there," she told me.

"Did you have to study lots and lots?" I asked.

Miss Jenkins laughed. "Yes, I guess I did study rather hard, Joyce. But I wanted to be a teacher, you know."

"Why did you want to be a teacher?" I asked her next.

"Because I like to teach, I suppose. And then I like boys and girls, and I want to help them learn."

That puzzled me. "You mean you *really* wanted to help us learn?" I asked. "And you are not teaching just because you had to do something?"

"Of course I wanted to do something, but I chose teaching because I thought I could help boys and girls most that way. You see, I want their minds to grow just as their bodies grow. That is a part of growing, too, you know."

I could not work very well and talk so much, but I did wonder about what Miss Jenkins had said.

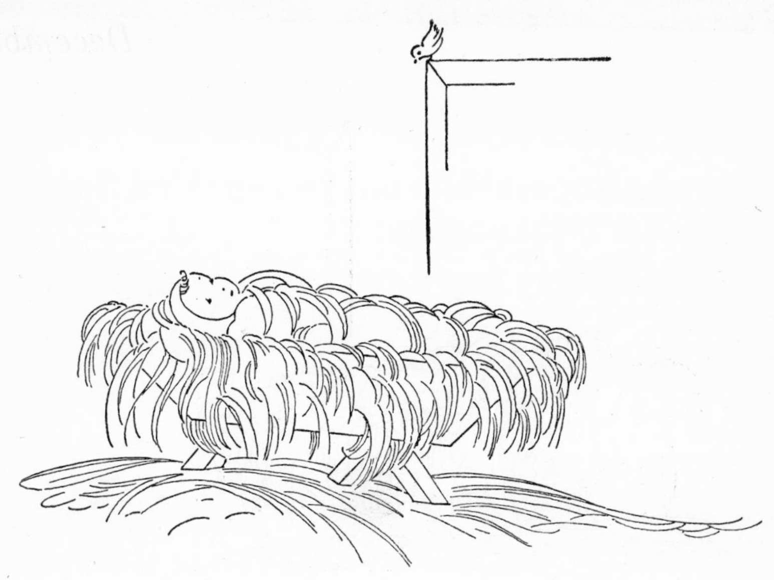

I had not thought about teachers wanting to help us learn before. I will try to study harder after this and make it easier for Miss Jenkins to teach me.

A Prayer of Thanks for Teachers

Thank you, God, for teachers who help our minds to grow. Help me to understand that growing that way is important, too. May I study my lessons well so that I can make it easier for my teachers to help me learn. Amen.

A Bible Verse to Remember

And Jesus advanced (grew) in wisdom and stature.

—Luke 2:52a.

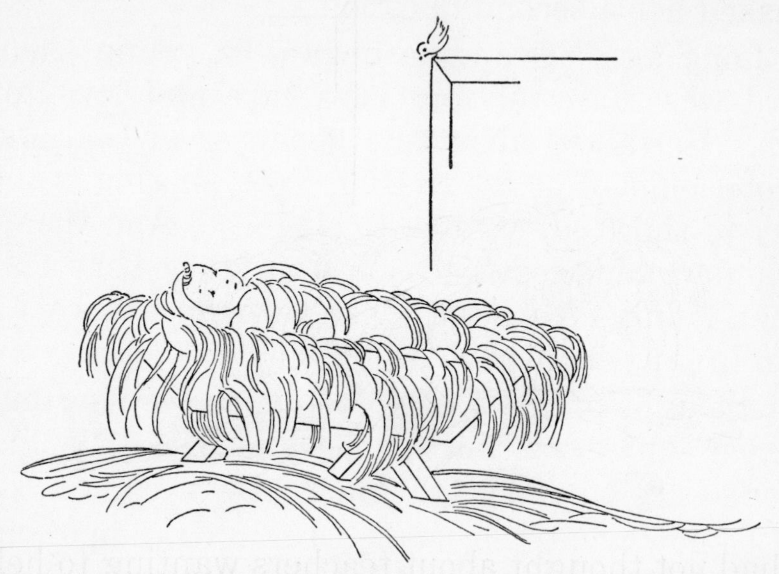

Songs of Praise

Grandma likes to sing while she is working. Her songs are all church songs. I like to hear her sing. She sounds so cheery and happy.

One day I said to her, "Grandma, I know you love God because you are always singing."

Grandma laughed. "And why should I not love God?" she said to me. "He has given me many fine things to enjoy. I have a good home here with you and your father and mother. I have good friends with whom I can visit. I have my health so that I am able to help your mother with the housework. And I have you to run errands for me. God is taking care of me in all of these ways."

"And is singing one way of being thankful?" I asked her a second question.

"Long ago," Grandma began, "a young shepherd was thankful for God's care and love for him. He talked about the goodness of God and wrote songs of praise to Him. Yes, singing is one way to show our thanks to God. . . . And then," Grandma added softly, "God seems to be very near when I sing. Almost as near as when I talk with him in prayer."

I thought of the way I feel when we sing our prayer songs or "How Strong and Sweet My Father's Care" in our department at church.

"I know what you mean," I told Grandma. "I feel that way, too, sometimes when I sing."

A Prayer of Gladness

I am glad, God, for your care for me. I am glad for the songs which tell me about your love and care. I like the quiet happy feeling I have when I sing them. Amen.

A Bible Verse to Remember

Oh sing unto the Lord a new song,
For he hath done marvelous things.

—Psalm 98:1.

Christmas Joy

I like the joys of Christmas-time—
The happy carols, and the chime
Of singing bells upon the air
Sprinkling gladness everywhere.

I like the spicy smell of pine,
The glow of candles, and the shine
Of colored balls upon the tree,
Hanging there so cheerily.

I like the friendly way we greet
Each other passing on the street,
And all the secret things we do
To make each other happy, too.

I am glad for every way
In which we honor Christmas Day.

A Christmas Prayer

Thank you, God, for the birthday of Jesus. Help me to plan to make someone happy at this Christmas-time. Help me to think of the gifts which I will give and not of the gifts which I want for myself. Show me ways of showing love to others. Amen.

A Bible Verse to Remember

For unto you is born this day in the city of David. a Saviour, who is Christ the Lord.

—Luke 2:11.

My Own Thoughts of God

My Own Thoughts of God